THE SUKHOI Su-27 *FLANKER*

Sometimes referred to as the "Flanker-D", the navalized Su-27 differs from the standard VVS configuration in having articulated canards, a retractable refueling probe on the left side of the fuselage ahead of the windscreen, a retractable tailhook, an IRST sensor offset to the right side of the windscreen, and numerous internal changes and modifications.

CREDITS:

This publication is the end product of contributions made on behalf of the authors and Aerofax, Inc. by the following: Michael Binder, Tom Copeland, Charles Fleming, Kelly Green, Tony Landis, Richard Pawloski, Alexei "Prost", Boris Rybak, Mikhail Simonov, Eva Smoke, Bernard Thouanel, Katsuhiko Tokunaga, Alexander Velovich, Achille Vigna and Barbara Wasson.

BACKGROUND:

The Sukhoi OKB (Design Bureau) takes its name from Pavel Osipovich Sukhoi, (b. July 10, 1895), its founder and director, who ran it from its formal rebirth during 1953 until his death at the age of 80 on September 15, 1975. Twice declared a Hero of Socialist labor, and a winner of the coveted Lenin and State prizes, Sukhoi graduated from the Moscow Higher Technical School during 1925 and began his aeronautical work with studies of experimental aircraft at the Moscow Aerodynamics Institute. He later was responsible for several bomber and attack aircraft designs, including the noteworthy Tupolev DB-2 (ANT-37) of mid-1930s vintage.

During 1938, Sukhoi established his own design bureau but, with the exception of the relatively unknown Su-2 attack aircraft, found little success and only minimal bureaucratic support. The bureau all but ceased to exist by 1949, and Sukhoi was forced to find employment once again under the aegis of Tupolev.

Stalin's death during 1953 removed bureaucratic and prejudicial issues that earlier had stood in Sukhoi's way, and by the end of the year, the long-maligned designer had been cleared by the administrator of aviation industry to reestablish his own bureau. This in fact took place and by 1954, at least two prototype jet powered supersonic fighters, the S (*Strelovidnyi*/sweptback) and T (*Treugoinyi*/triangular) aircraft, were under development. The S fighter led to the noteworthy Su-7 and the T fighter to the equally noteworthy Su-9, these setting precedent for the many Sukhoi designs to follow. In select instances, derivatives remain in the operational inventories of many world air forces, including that of the Soviet Union.

Since the mid-1950s, Sukhoi's bureau, along with the bureau founded by Artyom Mikoyan and Mikhail Gurevich (known universally as MIG), have been responsible for the design of virtually all significant Soviet Air Force (VVS) fighter and attack aircraft of the post-World War II era. Although never achieving the fame in the west that accompanied the MIG bureau's products, Sukhoi nevertheless produced numerous outstanding fighter/attack aircraft that eventually saw widespread service both in the VVS and many non-indigenous military services. A continuing evolutionary process, culminating in the subject of this book, the Su-27, now has brought Sukhoi into the spotlight as the primary bureau capable of competing one-on-one with MIG for VVS fighter supremacy.

On-going development of new and improved Sukhoi combat aircraft designs continues, with significant emphasis being placed on such esoterics as cost and profitability. The latter has been an outgrowth of *glasnost, peristroika,* and an associated Russian thrust in the direction of western capitalism. As of this writing, much has yet to be learned about future Soviet business initiatives and practices and as a result, it is difficult to predict the future direction of the bureau and its products. Additionally, there remain many peripheral elements that eventually will affect the state of the associated world political and economic climates and thus the status of all Soviet aircraft design bureaus as we know them today.

In the interim, complicating things for the

Jay Miller/Aerofax, Inc.

A total of eight "Flanker-As" or T-10s were built and test-flown prior to the construction of the first production aircraft. The prototype T-10 presently is displayed at Monino as part of the Soviet Air Force Museum.

An early production Su-27, "12", shortly after touchdown. Extended leading edge flaps and dark dielectric radome are noteworthy. Also visible are vertical tail dielectric panels.

"Flanker-B", "388" is the single-seat demonstration aircraft that has performed in a large number of western airshows with considerable regularity since 1989. Extreme length of towbar is noteworthy.

Maintenance personnel service "Flanker-B" "54". Noteworthy is maintenance being accommodated by ladder on right vertical tail. Dark green radome is commonplace on operational Su-27s.

Sukhoi—and other OKBs such as MIG—has been a well-hidden, but nevertheless noteworthy decline in aircraft design and production contracts resulting from the Soviet Union's overwhelming economic and social problems and a declining emphasis on defense. Sukhoi and MIG bureau chiefs General Designer[1] Mikhail Petrovich Simonov and General Designer and academician Rostislav Apollosovich Belyakov[2], respectively, have been confronted by a plethora of difficulites that are the end product of a lumbering transition into the age of Soviet capitalism and a deemphasized military force.

Regardless, Sukhoi's Simonov's capabilities as an engineer and bureau manager are not disputed. He has been rewarded for his skills by being elected—via popular vote—to the new USSR Congress of Peoples Deputies, and as a member of this, since has been elected as a representative to the Supreme Soviet. Simonov also serves on the Committee on Defense and State Security.

As Chairman of the Defense and State Security Committee, Simonov has been able to organize an experimental combination of research, development (the traditional role of the OKBs), and production facilities (traditionally separate from the OKBs) at Sukhoi to explore the merits of an autonomous bureau. One product of this new arrangement has been the bureau's Aerokonversia Association which is responsible for supersonic business jet development.

Simonov's attempt at OKB and production bureau restructuring is in direct response to the government's aspirations to make the Soviet economy not only more competitive internally, but externally and internationally, as well. All Soviet industry now must justify its continued existence based on its own merit and profits. Accordingly, because of their long-standing focus and total dependence upon government subsidy, the one dimensional design bureaus are finding it hard to make a profit when a totally unrelated bureau is being given the "production contract". Additionally, the present arrangement makes it more difficult to competitively market aircraft outside the Soviet Union.

SU-27:

Like the MIG-29, the Su-27 was conceived as a study during the mid-1970s when the VVS and associated aviation research institutes such as the TsAGI (Central Aerodynamic and Hydrodynamic Institute)[3] began to notice a trend in US fighter design resulting in improved maneuverability. Parallelling this was the integration of lessons learned by the US air services during air combat over Vietnam. In summary, it had been concluded that the "beyond visual range" (BVR) radar-guided air-to-air missile philosophy so highly regarded during the 1950s was not a viable proposition during the 1960s—and that the long-standing trend away from maneuverable fighters

---

[1] There are very distinct titles in the Soviet Design Bureaus, and elsewhere in Soviet industry. At the top is the General Designer followed by several Chief Designers (each usually responsible for a particular aircraft), then a variety of Deputy Chief Designers (each responsible for a functional area on a particular aircraft). It is interesting to note this hierarchy is beginning to break down as a result of the new thrust in the direction of capitalism and the requirement that Soviet enterprises, including design bureaus, must justify their existence on a pseudo-profit basis.

[2] As of early 1991, Belyakov was considering slowly transitioning the bureau into the hands of Deputy Designer Anatoly Belosvet.

[3] At the time the TsAGI was (and apparently still is) headed by Dr. Ivanovich Zagainov at the time, and upon last accounting employed a work force of over 10,000, including 2,000 scientific workers. Today, the TsAGI remains a formidable collection of wind tunnels and related test facilities, and still is located in the city of Zhukovsky, just outside Moscow (and not far from the famous Ramenskoye flight test facility).

The Su-27 is equipped with a substantial amount of vertical tail surface area to provide directional stability throughout its performance envelope. Ventral fins counter loss of stability in high-angle-of-attack conditions. Rudders are single-piece, hydraulically boosted surfaces.

and visual contact with the enemy was a nearly catastrophic mistake.

For the Soviets, whose aircraft had been on the receiving end of these new western developments, incentive to follow the same design trends emerged rapidly and with little fanfare. Though BVR capability was not ignored or rejected, a renewed emphasis on the more generic concept of the fighter was placed on new design studies and specifications. Close attention was paid to the new generation of western fighters that included the Grumman F-14, the McDonnell Douglas F-15, the General Dynamics F-16, and the McDonnell Douglas F/A-18, and applicable design trends were applied where appropriate. Trade-offs between range, maneuverability, structural materials, pilot physical limitations, payload, and other basic and specialized mission objectives generated a series of baseline specifications that effectively paralleled the new aircraft configurations then entering the US military inventory.

Heavy emphasis in new Soviet fighter designs was placed on the use of new materials and new technology (including computer generated archetypal models with optimum performance parameters), and the most basic objective—improved maneuverability—was given an extremely high priority. Additionally, special emphasis was placed on development of weapon systems that were considerably more capable and autonomous than any previously seen in the Soviet Union, and these, in turn, were integrated into the new airframes.

As the primary fighter design bureaus in the Soviet Union, both MIG and Sukhoi had been intimately involved with the TsAGI and other research facilities in their efforts to create a competitive new fighter generation. Considerable effort now was expended by both to provide designs falling within the performance paramenters of the new VVS-blessed specifications.

The resulting MIG design, eventually referred to as the MIG-29 (and described in *Aerofax Extra 2*) and codenamed *Fulcrum* by NATO, was moved rapidly from prototype to production following its first flight during October 1977. This aircraft was a direct response to the General Dynamics F-16 and thus was basically a small, lightweight fighter optimized for air combat. Somewhat short on range, it was nevertheless a major improvement over the MIG-21 and perhaps the first Soviet fighter since the late 1940s advent of the MIG-15 capable of operating one-on-one with its western counterparts.

Though superficially resembling the MIG-29, the other new Soviet fighter, the Sukhoi Su-27—assigned the NATO codename *Flanker*—initially was envisioned as a more refined and somewhat heavier air combat platform with considerably greater range and an improved beyond-visual-range weapons capability.

Both the MIG-29 and Su-27 attempted to leapfrog Soviet state-of-the-art in order to catch, or preferably surpass, the level of performance achieved by then-extant western fighters. Both were loosely based on western fighter design philosophy epitomized by the F-15 planform, but compromised in favor of Soviet materials and design technology. Soviet research, as it were, also had indicated the advantages of the F-15 configuration for highly maneuverable fighters. Various other technologies, especially turbofan engines and advanced avionics, also were selected for prioritized development.

Concerning the latter, both the MIG-29 and Su-27 pushed Soviet military aircraft technology forward with considerable rapidity—though not without considerable difficulty and expense. Turbofan engines were selected by the Soviets for much the same reasons as in the west—namely lower specific fuel consumption and a high thrust-to-weight ratio—but difficulties persisted in their development and operational utilization. Additionally, the advanced avionics suites that were

developed for the new aircraft were optimized to counter the extremely long range and look-down/shoot-down capabilities of the F-14 and F-15. Consequently, considerable time, money, and energy were expended on their development. Not surprisingly, the advantages of these propulsion and subsystems capabilities proved harder to realize for the Soviets due to limited computer technology and a greater reliance on manual versus automated production philosophies.

The Su-27 was designed by Simonov with the assistance of Sukhoi Chief Designer Oleg Sergayevich Samoylovich[4], who later left the OKB to become a Professor at the *Moskoviskiy Aviatsionniy Institute* (Moscow Aviation Institute). The first of eight T-10-1/Su-27 prototypes, after nearly two years development and construction, began its flight test program during early 1977, and was unwillingly revealed to the west as a result of US satellite surveillance of the Ramenskoye[5] flight test center. The results of this intelligence were published by the US Department of Defense (DoD) during the late 1970s and led to considerable speculation as to the aircraft's bureau of origin and performance capabilities.

The publicly released satellite imagery, purposefully degraded to avoid revealing the high quality of the originals, depicted an aircraft superficially resembling the F/A-18. As it was, the first aircraft, and the second prototype—which also was observed not long afterwards—were interim designs optimized only to explore the basic aerodynamics of the preliminary pre-production

<hr>

[4] Samoylovich also was the Chief Designer of the Su-24 and Su-25; at the time of initial Su-27 development, he was under bureau chief Evgeniy Ivanov who later was replaced by Mikhail Simonov.

[5] Ramenskoye now is referred to as the Zhukovsky flight test center. Major Soviet air bases and flight test facilities tend to be named after the largest town or city in their vicinity. Zhukovsky now is considerably larger than Ramenskoye and thus the famous flight test center has been renamed.

Aerofax, Inc. collection

Fully-armed operational "Flanker-B" equipped with several different long and short burn AA-10 "Alamo" air-to-air missile configurations. Barely visible are centerline-mounted "Alamos".

Jay Miller/Aerofax, Inc.

The "Flanker-B" is an extremely pleasing design with exceptionally well defined aerodynamics. Demonstration aircraft shown has Sukhoi logo visible underneath Soviet star on vertical tail.

configuration.

Though western intelligence assessments predicted the new Sukhoi fighter to achieve operational service no later than 1982, it was to be nearly ten years before actual operational deployment took place. In the interim, the aircraft underwent a major redesign effort which, in retrospect, was quite reminiscent of that which occurred to the YF-17 and its follow-on production version, the F/A-18.

The original prototypes, which were considerably smaller and decidedly less refined aerodynamically than the production aircraft to follow, had a significant amount of wing and leading edge extension blending, rounding of the leading edge at the wingtips, a more abbreviated fuselage and nose contour, apparently smaller engines, less pronounced positioning of the intakes, more inboard placement of the vertical tail surfaces, a stubby empennage, and many other differences that eventually led observers to accurately conclude that the prototypes were totally different aircraft from their successors.

In the production configured aircraft, which were not observed for nearly a decade following discovery of the prototypes, the wingtips became square and acquired missile launching rails, the vertical stabilizers were moved to the outer edges of the engine nacelles and reshaped, the nose contour was lengthened and greatly refined, the centrally located tailcone between the engines grew in size and changed shape dramatically (indicating the Soviets experienced significant empennage drag difficulties; in the case of the Su-27, however, the lengthened and enlarged tail-

cone provided an excellent location for mounting electronic countermeasures equipment, tail warning sensors, and expendable electronic warfare dispensers), and the ventrally located airbrake assembly was replaced by a dorsally mounted unit quite similar to that seen on the F-15.

Unlike the MIG-29, the Su-27, as it grew in terms of capability and requirement, also was victimized by its weapon system and, as many sources later would claim, was delayed in service entry primarily as a result of weapon system deficiencies. Though little information pertaining to the Su-27's advanced weapon system has surfaced in the west, it is apparent that the radar and associated fire control system, which purportedly has a commendable look-down/shoot-down capability, is large and powerful. Analysts have been able to assess some of the aircraft's capability simply by estimating such items as aircraft size, weight, and nose cross-sectional area. Many sources also have stated problems with the sophisticated look-down/shoot-down coherent-pulse Doppler radar system contributed to the aircraft's exceptionally long development cycle.

Shortly after the Su-27 reached full scale production in a plant in the Komsomolsk Khabarovsk territory (located in the eastern USSR), serious problems of a non-weapon systems related nature are thought to have occurred. These included difficulties with the fuel supply system, stability anomalies related to basic aerodynamics, and propulsion system failures. These anomalies led to a temporary cessation of production during mid-1986. Reportedly, at one point several dozen Su-27s were stored at Komsomolsk in a partially

completed state while solutions to the aircraft's problems were developed. It is unclear if the problems resulted in accidents, or simply hindered operations to an unacceptable extent.

In the interim, the TsAGI was, as per standard practice, consulted in an effort to solve the aerodynamic anomalies. At the same time it was also asked to participate in the development of laws for the fly-by-wire flight control system. The latter was a first for a production Soviet fighter and thus an item of particular importance both to Sukhoi and the TsAGI.

Initial deployment of the Su-27 was made to the Kola Peninsula, in the far northern Murmansk region of the Soviet Union. As operational experience increased with the type, it began flying in conjunction with Ilyushin Il-76 *Mainstay* AEW&C aircraft and from late 1986 on, became particularly active in simulated interceptions of NATO aircraft over the Barents Sea.

The Su-27 is considerably larger than the MiG-29, and is reportedly equipped with a more sophisticated fire-control system. Surprisingly it is thought to be only 10 to 15 percent more expensive to produce than its Mikoyan stablemate, mainly because it uses conventional materials in its construction, whereas the MiG uses some composites and exotic alloys.

By comparison with the MiG-29, the production Su-27 seemed, on first appearance to western analysts during the 1989 Paris Airshow, to be too large. Several feet longer than the F-14, it was not expected to be particularly maneuverable in combat and was considered more of a long-range BVR interceptor than a dog fighter. All of this changed, however, following the aircraft's first appearances at a western airshow. During its initial public flight display at Paris during 1989, it not only was maneuverable, it was stunningly nimble.

Much of this later was attributed to its rudimentary fly-by-wire flight control system. Though based on analog rather than digital technology, it obviously was sufficiently capable to accommodate the Su-27's flight control system needs, and to do so with reasonable finesse and harmony.

Beyond the flight control system, the real technology leap made by the Su-27 was its fire-control system. A powerful track-while-scan coherent-pulse Doppler look-down/shoot-down radar was installed in the large nose of the aircraft, giving it much greater capability than the smaller MIG-29. Equipped with an approx. 3 ft. 4 in. dia. (1 m.) flat-plate antenna, the radar was reported to have a search range of 150 mi. (240 km.) and a tracking range of 115 mi. (185 km.).

The improving quality of Soviet aircraft, directly attributable to the integration of pirated western technology, has been of serious concern to the west for some time. Not only have the basic range and payload capabilities of Soviet aircraft increased fourfold since the first jet fighter generation, but a viable multi-role capability has emerged. Parallelling this has been an increase in mission autonomy and a reduced reliance upon ground-based central control systems.

Conversely, the trend in the west has been in the opposite direction. Though US propaganda for years had underscored the autonomy of US fighters and their pilots, in truth they always have been interfaced with a ground control or airborne intercept system of one kind or another. Today, the use of such systems continues, though on a much more sophisticated level. The Soviet trend thus echoes the western, though in inverse fashion.

In a bizarre turn, while the west once belittled the Soviets for their dependence upon rigid command and control structures, the influence of modern weapons and sensors now has begun to drive the west toward a similar logic. The advent of the Airborne Warning and Control System (AWACS), and the need to fuse sensor information from various platforms and to data link that information to all applicable aircraft, has made the west adopt a centralized control philosophy that less than two decades ago would have been anathema to extant US military operational concepts.

It remains a matter of debate if the fourth generation Soviet fighters represented by the Su-27 and MIG-29 are a technological breakthrough that negates the advantage the west always has managed to maintain. It certainly took the Soviets a shorter period of time to close the gap than many western analysts believed possible, though this probably was aggravated by a general slowing of defense research (at least in tactical areas) in the west. Though neither the Su-27 nor the MIG-29 have weapons systems comparable to that found in either the F-14 or F-15, the absolute and decisive technological superiority once enjoyed by the western fighters has clearly been seriously eroded.

The first publicly released photographs of an operational Su-27 were taken by the crew of a Norwegian Air Force Lockheed P-3B of No. 333 Squadron on September 13, 1987. Two Su-27s were launched to intercept and escort the P-3B, each armed with six AA-10 air-to-air missiles of three different models. One of the Su-27s reportedly maneuvered to within 32 ft. (10 m.) of the P-3B, and then moved 160 ft. (50 m.) in front of it. According to the Norwegian crew the *Flanker* then engaged its afterburner. The P-3B was able to avoid the severe turbulence caused by the afterburner's significant exhaust blast, and no damage was incurred.

Sometime later during the same intercept, the Su-27 and P-3B touched. The left tail of the Su-27 came in contact with the P-3B's outer starboard propeller, resulting in fragments that penetrated the P-3B's fuselage. This led to the Norwegians filing a formal protest with the Soviet Union over the incident. The Norwegian Defense Ministry said the *Orion* was on a routine patrol/surveillance sortie over the Barents Sea when the Su-27 approached "... less than two meters ..." from its port side. This otherwise routine intercept in international airspace broke the standard protocol between NATO and the Warsaw Pact about such encounters. A subsequent report by a Norwegian investigating committee put the blame squarely on the pilot of the Su-27. The Norwegians believed that the incident resulted from bad judgment and airmanship by the Soviet pilot, and did not represent a deliberate attempt to ram the *Orion*. Soviet allegations that the P-3B pilot had made a dangerous maneuver were categorically denied by the Norwegians. Total damage to the *Orion* involved four propeller blades, three holes through the fuselage, and a large dent. The total cost to repair the aircraft was estimated to be $130,000 US.

The DoD estimates that by October 1986, only five Su-27s had achieved operational service with the *Voyska PVO,* plus another ten in the Soviet tactical forces. The total had increased to over 50 by mid-1987 at which time the production rate was estimated at two aircraft per month. By early 1989, the estimates had grown to over 200 Su-27s in service with several Soviet organizations. More than 100 had entered service with the Soviet Strategic Air Defense Forces, replacing older types such as the Yak-28P, Su-15 and Tu-28P. These were based mainly at the Strategic Air Forces Headquarters at Legnica (Poland, Western TVD) and Vinnitsa (Ukraine, South Western TVD).

The primary mission of the aircraft assigned to the Strategic Air Force is thought be be the long range escort of Su-24 *Fencer* interdiction aircraft. Additional duties include, of course, conventional

long-range interception of threat aircraft.

During various airshows held at Paris and elsewhere around the world, the Su-27 has demonstrated that it is capable of controlled flight at AoAs well beyond those normally used by contemporary western fighter aircraft. When Sukhoi Chief Test Pilot Viktor Georgiyevich Pugachev first performed what since has been named the "Pugachev Cobra" at the 1989 Paris Air Show, western observers were stunned. None had previously witnessed an aircraft of the size and performance capability of the Su-27 perform such a bizarre aerial gambit. The result was a major publicity coup for the Soviet contingent.

Considerable analysis of the "Pugachev Cobra" was undertaken by western analysts following its initial unveiling—primarily to assess its applicability to air combat. After reviewing considerable video footage of the maneuver wherein the aircraft pitched up from level flight some 120° until the nose was well past the vertical (and the aircraft was flying, very briefly, tail first) and then pitched forward again to a level attitude, with a significant loss of forward speed and without appreciable gain or loss of altitude, the consensus of opinion remained divided as to whether it had "real world" applicability. Compounding the assessment's

value was the question addressing the operational status of the demonstration aircraft—which obviously had been modified somewhat from Su-27's found in VVS front line service. The demonstration aircraft, for instance, apparently had been stripped of its weapons system to lower weight, though Pugachev earlier had stated the aircraft did in fact carry all its operational equipment complement except for external armament.[6]

The Soviets have explained that the "Cobra" maneuver imposes g-loads of only 3.5 to 4 on the aircraft. Entry speed for the maneuver must be below 250 mph (402 km/h) and the speed is reduced to about 70 mph (113 km/h) in about 3 seconds. The maneuver is entered when the pilot pulls the stick full aft, holding it in that position for a short period, then pushing it full forward to recover. During the maneuver, the automatic AoA limiter is manually overridden. Almost continuous positive tailplane angles observed during aerobatic maneuvering suggest the aircraft has

---

[6] Most western analysts questioned Pugachev's statement as they claim it is doubtful the Soviets would allow the Su-27's sensitive weapons system to venture to a public airshow. Additionally, a review of the airshow circuit Su-27's instrument panel reveals that the fire control system panel has been removed.

All of the known "Flanker" variants are equipped with a dorsally-mounted, hydraulically-actuated airbrake hinged at its forward end. This system is effective and usable up to .9 Mach.

A pair of stock, operational "Flankers" during formation maneuvers. The aircraft are not missile equipped. Due to the aircraft's inherent exceptional range, external fuel tanks are a rarely utilized option.

Aerofax, Inc. collection

The ''Flanker's'' wing pylons are somewhat unusual in having a webbed mounted assembly rather than the more conventional single piece design. Su-27 ''05'' is seen without missiles during a training sortie.

a large degree of built-in static instability.

The ''Cobra'' maneuver now has been demonstrated repeatedly by both the Su-27 and the MIG-29 at a variety of international airshows and related events. As noted previously, there remains no clear consensus as to specifically the tactical benefits afforded an aircraft that can perform this trick. Most western pilots do seem to agree that the maneuver would take any attacker by surprise the first time it was performed, but its novelty would quickly wear off. Exactly how a western pilot would respond in combat is unclear, but the tactical advantage for the Soviet pilot, if it exists at all, apparently is small.

According to Soviet pilots, the maneuver originally was developed as part of a test program to assist in determining the upper limit angle of attack for the Su-27 flight control system.[7] When

---

[7] Furthering the dispute between the MIG and Sukhoi OKBs, it should be mentioned here that MIG Chief Test Pilot Valery Menitsky maintains that the ''Cobra'' maneuver was developed at the TsAGI using the MIG-29, and then ''stolen'' by Sukhoi and Pugachev for the Paris Airshow.

the aircraft was cleared by the Soviet government to go to Paris, the Sukhoi pilots wanted a maneuver that would impress the western press and officials, and thus incorporated the ''Cobra'' into the airshow routine. Sukhoi officials have stated that the keys to the maneuver lie in the aircraft's ability to maintain symmetrical airflow over the wings and fuselage and in its ability to maintain sufficient airflow to the engines in order to prevent flameout. The auxiliary ventral intake doors fitted to the Su-27 appear critical to the latter requirement.

Since its Paris debut, Australian, Canadian and US pilots have performed the ''Cobra'' maneuver both intentionally and unintentionally in the McDonnell Douglas F/A-18 Hornet and the General Dynamics F-16. Performing the ''Cobra'' is not considered routine, however, and it is prohibited under normal flight circumstances for both aircraft. In the case of the F-16, modifications to the aircraft's fly-by-wire flight control system were required for the maneuver to be properly executed.

During late 1989 and prior to actually performing the maneuver in the F/A-18, McDonnell

Douglas completed a series of ''Cobra'' tests in the F/A-18 simulator. Though results of those tests remain proprietary as of this writing, McDonnell Douglas acknowledges that by moving the *Hornet's* center of gravity slightly aft (but still within published limits), the simulator achieved 100° from the horizontal with an 85° AoA while gaining only 250 ft. (78 m.) altitude. In order to accomplish the simulation, the pitch rate feedback was disabled in the flight control system.

The Su-27 also has demonstrated the tail-slide maneuver first performed by the MiG-29 at the 1988 Farnborough airshow. This maneuver has been dubbed ''the Cloche'' (French for ''bell'') by the Soviets. The Su-27 climbed more steeply into the maneuver than the MiG-29, and also held its nose-up attitude longer.

The Su-27 is designed for rough field operations and has both retractable debris protection grids in the engine inlets and a somewhat over-designed and rugged landing gear. Part of the latter's design philosophy was to permit the aircraft to be operated by relatively inexperienced pilots (who tend to make hard landings). Large, over-inflated tires are part of this design approach.

The Su-27 can be equipped with self-starters for the engines, and has a large battery capacity, decreasing its dependence on ground support equipment during forward deployments. Ground support equipment in general required for the Su-27 in the field is minimal due to the design's innate self-sufficiency. Considerable emphasis has been placed on remote operations.

Seven Su-27 variants have been identified to date:

Flanker-A or T-10: Initial eight prototypes observed at the Ramenskoye flight test center. The first flight of the first aircraft took place on May 20, 1977 with Maj. Gen. Vladimir Ilyushin as pilot. These basically were aerodynamic testbeds for the later production configuration. Vortices generated at the wing roots with this prototype configuration could potentially drastically reduce the effectiveness of the vertical stabilizers during sideslips at high angles of attack. The decision on production aircraft to move the vertical surfaces out to the fuselage edges allowed the vortices to stream back well inside of these surfaces. The trade-off was that the outboard location could provoke early bursting of the strake vortices as they passed the wing trailing edge, resulting in a slight loss of lift.

The empennage configuration between the

Operational ''Flanker-B'', ''05'' with the standard green vertical fin dielectric tips, vertical fin dielectric panels, and nose radome. Some images of this aircraft, however, seem to show a black, rather than green radome. This aircraft also is equipped with the standard complement of AA-10 air-to-air missiles.

engines initially a flat, tapered surface with a small, cone-like projection, went through a wide variety of designs before a satisfactory planform was found. There are reports that the initial two aircraft (the T-10s) were not fitted with the production aircraft's sophisticated fly-by-wire flight control system and instead used a conventional mechanical arrangement. These prototypes are believed to have been powered by two Tumansky R-29 turbojets of 28,100 lbs. (12,746 kg.) th. at sea level. Although slightly more powerful than the Lyulka AL-31F turbofan engines fitted to production aircraft, these engines had a higher specific fuel consumption and were decidedly less reliable.

Flanker-B: This is the initial production version, with square wingtips mounting launchers for AA-10 air-to-air missiles, although none have been observed at this location. The vertical stabilizers were moved to the outer edges of the engine nacelles, similar to the F-15. Large ventral fins, conceptually similar to the initial F-15 design before it actually was built, were fitted immediately below the dorsals. An extended (approximately 4 ft.) tailcone between the engines provides volume for ECM equipment and expendables such as flares and chaff. This variant is the first production Soviet fighter to be fitted with a fly-by-wire flight control system. The initial flight of the *Flanker*-B was on April 20, 1981, nearly four years after the first T-10 prototype flew.

The single-seat Su-27 has a fuel fraction of 45%, which is better than many contemporary western fighters. It carries up to 22,000 pounds of fuel internally, giving a maximum range of 2,580 miles. It is not fitted with an in-flight refueling system.

Flanker-B2/-D: First mentioned in early 1988 by Rear Admiral William O. Studeman, US Director of Naval Intelligence. This variant is intended for service on the Soviet Navy's large flat-deck aircraft carriers. The first ship in this latter class, the *Tbilisi*[8], was laid down at the Nikolayev South ship yards during mid-1983 and was launched on December 5, 1985. However, planning for this and several sister ships goes back much further, with Soviet Admiral Gorshkov acknowledging them as early as 1979. The Nikolayev South yards have the only ways in the Soviet Union capable of accommodating such large ships, and the manufacturing teams there had gained substantial previous experience during the construction of the *Kiev* class of cruiser/carriers. *Tbilisi* sea trials commenced during early 1988, and western analysts now expect the ship to become operational during 1992. A second ship of this class was laid down during December 1985, after the *Tbilisi* cleared the ways.

The flight deck of the 75,000 ton *Tbilisi* is 240 ft. (74.8 m.) wide and approximately 984 ft. (306.7 m.) long. The hanger deck is 610 ft. (190.1 m.) by 98 ft. (30.5 m.) by 25 ft. (7.8 m.), and is capable of holding up to 50 aircraft. There are two deck-edge elevators and a single elevator immediately beside the superstructure. This makes the ship roughly the same size as the USS *Forrestal*-class (CV-59) conventional carriers. The flight deck also is equipped with arresting gear and barricades. Power for the ship is provided by two nuclear reactors and steam turbines, delivering approximately 200,000 shp to four propellers. The ship is thought to be capable of 32 knots, which is roughly the same as the newer US carriers.

In addition to the navalized Su-27, navalized variants of the MIG-29 and Su-25 also are undergoing development for deployment aboard the new Soviet carriers. These will replace the Yak-36 *Forger* V/STOL aircraft used on the previous

[8] There have been reports that this vessel will carry the name *Leonid Brezhnev* when it enters service during 1992.

"Flanker-B", "388" immediately prior to demonstration during 1990 Oklahoma City, Oklahoma airshow. White radome and miscellaneous dielectric panels are non-standard for type.

Operational Su-27s, including "Flanker-As", "57" and "58", at an unidentified airfield near Moscow. Noteworthy is ventral missile pylon/rail assembly. Unit marking at base of vertical tail is unidentified.

The Su-27, in cruise configuration and armed with at least two different versions of the AA-10 "Alamo" air-to-air missile. Markings are standard for type including large red "33" below windscreen.

Soviet *Kiev* class cruiser-carriers.

The navalized variant of the *Flanker* is fitted with movable foreplanes to allow a high AoA during landing, lowering the aircraft's approach speed to approximately 130 knots. An unfortunate by-product of the canard installation is that it has made the aircraft somewhat unstable at low speeds. Foldable wings also are installed on the navalized Su-27 to ease deck handling and storage. The landing gear has been strengthened, and an arresting hook has been added to the underside of the rear fuselage. An in-flight refueling capability using an installation similar to the western hose-and-drogue system has been installed. The aircraft also is reported to be able to carry a "buddy" system refueling pod similar to those carried by US Navy aircraft and recent photos indicate also that a photo reconnaissance pod has been developed for Su-27 centerline installation.

The *Tbilisi* class carriers use a 7° inclined ramp at their bow instead of catapults, similar to that fitted to several British and Indian carriers. This eliminates the need for catapult system accommodations on the fighters. Both the Su-27 and MIG-29 have relatively short take-off runs with nor-

mal fuel and full afterburners, and are considered suitable for jump-ramp operations. It is doubtful, however, that either aircraft can carry a full weapons load when using this launch method. The Soviets are reportedly working on a hydraulic catapult to assist heavier aircraft when launching from future ships of this class.

Viktor Pugachev made 13 landings on the *Tbilisi* during late 1989 in the course of the initial Su-27 carrier qualification trails. The MiG-29 also was carrier qualified at the same time by Mikoyan Deputy Chief Test Pilot Anatole Kvotchur. Additional Su-27 landings were made by other pilots immediately after Pugachev qualified the aircraft.

Sukhoi General Designer Mikhail Simonov discussed the modified fighter with *Aviation Week and Space Technology* during early 1990. During this interview he stated that it was thought wiser to modify an existing airframe for the Navy role rather than create an entirely new aircraft. He felt that later, after the Soviet Navy had acquired experience in carrier operations, specialized and dedicated Navy aircraft might be contemplated, prototyped, and produced—but not before the economics of doing so could be justified.

Flanker-C (Su-27UB): Tandem two-seat version

Aerofax, Inc. collection

"Flanker-B", "01", during intercept off the Norwegian coast. Fully-extended airbrake underscores the fact that this deceleration device can be used throughout the aircraft's subsonic flight envelope.

of *Flanker*-B. This version retains the full combat capabilities of the single-seat aircraft and is routinely deployed as a long-endurance interceptor. Slightly taller (20 ft. 10.25 in. [6.5 m.]) vertical stabilizers are fitted to overcome moderate loss of directional stability caused by the elevated canopy design.

It is not clear if the Su-27UB shares the "simulator" capability reportedly built into the MIG-29UB. The *Fulcrum's* rear seat is capable of functioning as an airborne simulator, allowing the instructor (who always sits in back) to simulate system failures, mode changes, radar targets, infrared targets, etc. for the student in the front seat. The student flies the appropriate intercept profiles and maneuvers in accordance with a training script, based on the presentations on his displays. Several recorders are fitted to the aircraft to debrief stick and throttle movements, radar display information and the like, once the student and instructor are back on the ground. This technology apparently came about because the Soviets could not gain access to the large-scale computers necessary to produce the simulators used by western nations. Some western analysts feel this con-

cept may provide a superior method of conducting some types of training.

STOL-*Flanker* (also referred to as the T-10-24): A single Su-27 has been modified with forward canards and vectorable engine nozzles for a test program similar to that being conducted by the F-15S/MTD aircraft. It is expected that this test program eventually will result in a production short take-off and landing version of the Su-27. The aircraft also is being used as a research aircraft to explore possible future fighter designs, including second-generation carrier-based aircraft. It is not clear as to weather the canards are fully integrated into the aircraft's fly-by-wire flight control system, but the consensus of western opionion is that they are.

P-42: A specially prepared Su-27 optimized for assaults on various world time-to-climb records. This aircraft, which as of this writing is being flown from the Ramenskoye flight test facility, has been stripped of all superfluous items including paint, its ventral fins, its vertical fin tips, and many internal items related to its normal operational capability. Additionally, its wings have been shortened, there are no missile launch rails, and

the composite nose radome has been replaced by a solid aluminum fairing.

Flown by Sukhoi Chief Test Pilot Viktor Pugachev, the P-42 set a world record by climbing to 9,625 ft. (3,000 m.) in 25.373 seconds on October 27, 1986, beating by two seconds the then extant record held by a specially prepared McDonnell Douglas F-15A during *Project Streak Eagle*. On November 15, Pugachev claimed another record by taking the P-42 to 19,250 ft. (6,000 m.) in 37.050 seconds, again bettering the existing *Streak Eagle* record by a little over two seconds. On March 10, 1987, N. F. Sadovnikov flew the P-42 to 28,875 ft. (9,000 m.) in 44.176 seconds and to 38,500 ft. (12,000 m.) in 55.542 seconds. In both cases, the new times exceeded the *Streak Eagle* claims by a little over four seconds.

Data submitted with the claim for the November records gave the powerplant as two TR-32U turbofans, each rated at 29,955 lbs. (13,587 kg.) th. w/afterburning. These engines are assumed to be a development of the Tumansky R-29 turbojets used in the initial *Flanker*-A prototypes. A total of 27 world records for time-to-climb and level flight altitude eventually were claimed by the P-42 from 1986 to 1988.

***Flanker*-"C-2":** During 1990, a single photo was released by Tass showing an unusually modified Su-27 with a totally new chined nose, side-by-side seating for two crew (the cockpit area looks suspiciously similar to that seen on the Su-24), articulated canards, and no ventral fins. Little is known about this aircraft but it is suspected to be possibly a one-off training configuration optimized for carrier operations. Some sources, however, claim a production potential for this aircraft with special systems optimized for ground attack.

Foreign Sales: Though there have been a considerable number of rumors pertaining to non-indigenous Su-27 sales, to date, imagery of Su-27 in non-Soviet markings has yet to surface. Among the many countries reported to have received the aircraft is Iraq—though confirmation is lacking and the *Flanker* is not known to have participated in the recent Gulf War. "Aerospace Daily" announced on July 5, 1989 that the Soviets had agreed to sell the *Flanker* to Iraq, although no quantities or delivery dates were provided. This was the first announced sale of the aircraft outside the Soviet bloc. The *International Defense Intelligence Weekly* reported in its September 25, 1989 volume that Afghanistan had taken delivery of unspecified quantities of MiG-29 and Su-27 aircraft, and on February 28, 1990, *Flight International* noted that India and Finland were exploring Su-27 acquisition options. Underscoring this interest, at least two Su-27s were demonstrated in New Delhi on their way back to Moscow after being displayed at Asian Aerospace '90. In the same article it was noted that the Indian Navy was "seen as a likely candidate to receive the aircraft". On March 22, 1991, it was announced by the Soviet and Chinese governments that an agreement would lead to the delivery of Su-27s to the Chinese air force by year's end.

To date, in the interest of furthering relations with the western democracies, five western pilots have been afforded the opportunity to fly the Su-27. The first was Ray Funnell, Chief of the Australian Air Force; the second was a Singapore Air Force General who piloted the aircraft at the Singapore Airshow during February of 1990; the third was an unidentified US female aerobatic pilot who flew the aircraft during an airshow at Oklahoma City, Oklahoma during the summer of 1990; the fourth was David M. North, Managing Editor of *Aviation Week & Space Technology* who flew it during the 1990 Farnborough Airshow; and

Dick Pawloski collection

Recently, images such as this one of a "Flanker-B" firing rockets from a rocket pod have served to verify that the type has at least a limited air-to-ground capability.

the fifth was Sir Peter Harding, Air Chief Marshall of the Royal Air Force who also flew it during the 1990 Farnborough Airshow.

Future Su-27 developments that have been alluded to by Sukhoi personnel include aircraft with improved technology airframes incorporating advanced composites and refined aerodynamics. Additionally, cockpit upgrades also are scheduled, these including four "glass"-type multi-function-displays (MFDs) to replace the current analog instrumentation, a side-stick controller in place of the current centrally-mounted stick, and inflight refueling capability.

General Designer Simonov, during the 1989 Paris Airshow, noted that two Su-27s—a single-seat and a two-seat aircraft—had been modified to incorporate a retractable inflight refueling probe on the port side of their respective noses. Endurance flights with these testbeds included missions lasting up to sixteen hours and traversing, on one occasion, a distance of 8,700 miles (14,000 km.—from Moscow to the Soviet Pacific coast and back). Refueling was accomplished utilizing an Il-yushin Il-78 tanker and a Sukhoi Su-24 equipped with a buddy refueling pack.

Aerofax, Inc. collection

Su-27, "52", taxiing out for departure on practice intercept mission. Massive (for a fighter) radome is readily apparent in this view. Noteworthy are ventral pylons and extended leading edge flaps.

CONSTRUCTION AND SYSTEMS:

Like the MIG-29, the Su-27 officially is described by the US Department of Defense as a supersonic all-weather counter-air fighter. It is equipped with a look-down/shoot-down weapons system and BVR air-to-air missiles, and has a limited secondary ground attack role. The Su-27's range, thrust-to-weight ratio, and maneuverability are all significant improvements over earlier Soviet fighters. Its large coherent-pulse Doppler radar and heavy armament give it formidable capabilities against low flying aircraft and cruise missiles, particularly when it is deployed in partnership with the Soviet *Mainstay* Airborne Early Warning and Control (AEW&C) aircraft. The DoD estimates a combat radius for the Su-27 at least as great as that of the Tupolev Tu-28P *Fiddler*, which is long overdue for replacement and is being retired from service as Su-27s become available. Demise of the

Tu-28P gives the Su-27 an additional escort role for cruise-missile armed bombers and deep penetration attack aircraft on sorties against the UK and western Europe.

Fuselage: The fuselage is a basically circular cross-section semi-monocoque all-metal structure, sloping down, and tapering sharply, immediately aft of the canopy as it fairs into the wing and engine interfacing assemblies. The empennage section is extremely narrow in cross-section and serves to support the passive tail warning sensors, antenna for the instrument landing system, a chaff and flare dispenser unit, and the drag chute compartment. There is considerable use of titanium in the load-bearing structures with aluminum alloy skin and subassemblies throughout the fuselage component. The fuselage flattens behind the

cockpit and blends into the wings via the leading edge extensions. The latter, sometimes referred to as "lexes", generate vortices that energize the airflow over the outer wing panels, consequently significantly increasing lift.

Cockpit: The cockpit is set high on the forward uselage and is fitted with a large three-piece canopy with low sills. The canopy arrangement affords excellent all-round visibility. The two-seat aircraft has a noticeable bulge in the extended aft transparency to provide additional headroom and improved forward visibility for the rear seat occupant. Rear-view mirrors are attached to the canopy hoop frame. The rear-hinged canopies open vertically via a hydraulic actuator.

A helmet mounted target designation system is available and is seen primarily in the operational

Inverted pass by demo Su-27, "388". Airshow routine using this aircraft remains a spectacular event. Despite its size, the "Flanker" is extraordinarily nimble. Assymetrical use of wing trailing edge and horizontal tail surfaces provides exceptional roll rates. Symmetrical use of horizontal tail surfaces provides exceptional pitch control.

Full-afterburner takeoff of two ''Flanker-As''. Noteworthy are fully-extended leading edge flaps, landing gear position just prior to retraction process, and exceptional quantity of combustion materials seen in the form of smoke at the aft end of the aircraft. Such ''dirty'' exhaust is a point against this and other Soviet aircraft because increased visibility.

version of the single-seat aircraft. A heads-up display (HUD) is located in the center of the front cockpit and incorporates data from the radar and IRST (infrared search and track) into a coordinated display. Below the HUD there is a 10-station weapons pylon selector panel with a radar/IRST computer-generated display to starboard. Later aircraft have a wide-angle HUD, similar to that fitted in recent western aircraft. Initial production Su-27s have a HUD with a somewhat narrower field of view.

Early aircraft also used conventional instrumentation consisting of the normal analog flight control and engine instruments in a mostly conventional arrangement. The lower right portion of the instrument panel was occupied by an unsophisticated radar warning/missile launch warning indicator based on a plan-view of the aircraft with segmented warning indicators.

Early production aircraft were fitted with a conventional center-mounted control stick, but aircraft produced starting in mid-1989 are fitted with a side-stick-controller mounted on the right side of the cockpit, similar to that of the General Dynamics F-16. These later aircraft also are fitted with a multi-function display (MFD) equipped instrument panel. An EFIS-equipped (electronic flight instrumentation system) prototype was flown for almost two years prior to committing the MFD system to production.

In a situation similar to that faced by western aircraft designers, Sukhoi engineers appear to have had difficulties deciding what information needs to be displayed on the Heads-Up Display and the various in-cockpit MFDs during various stages of flight. Several software updates have been delivered to operational squadrons as feedback from pilots has been assimilated.

The standard Su-27 configuration utilizes a quadruple-redundant fly-by-wire flight control system incorporating AoA and g-load limiters. The normal AoA limit is 30° to 35°, but the limiters can be manually overridden for any given maneuver. According to most sources, the fly-by-wire system uses analog computers for virtually all functions. Like many state-of-the-art combat aircraft, the Su-27 is statically unstable, and a sophisticated

fly-by-wire system is required to control the aircraft during all phases of flight.

In a novel approach to pilot safety, Sukhoi engineers have developed and installed in production Su-27s what now is referred to as the ''panic button''. This manually activated switch is mounted on the pilot's control stick. Whenever the pilot feels the aircraft is in a maneuver from which he can not recover, depressing this switch instructs the autopilot to return the aircraft to wings-level, right-side-up flight.

The K-36MD zero/zero ejection seat used in both single-seat and two-seat *Flankers* uses a thrust vector control system on its rocket engine to control the direction of escape from the aircraft. In almost all cases the seat will automatically seek ''up'', although the seats in the Su-27UB are programmed to angle away from each other during simultaneous ejections.

The K-36MD ejection seat is provided with rigid, rod-extended stabilizing chutes, a damper, and integral service systems. All this ensures position stability and low inertial and upstream impacts on the pilot after ejection. The seat can safely eject the pilot at altitudes from zero to 81,840 ft. (25 km.), and at speeds from zero to 870 mph (1,400 km/h) or Mach 3.0 (808 mph [1,300 km/h] or Mach 2.5 in situations where the pilot is wearing light equipment with only a crash helmet and an oxygen mask).

An automatic seat harness positions the pilot in the optimum ejection pose. The harness includes arm side spread limiters, shoulder and waist straps, and leg straps with lifting jacks. The ejection is effected by means of a combined thrust unit incorporating a two-tube ejection gun and a rocket engine producing a 1,389 lb./ft. (630 kg./ft.) pulse. The recovery chute is packed in the seat head-rest and is extracted and deployed automatically by a reliable squib mechanism which also will cut off the harness straps and release the seat from the pilot. At high speeds, the chute is deployed with a minimum delay that is varied smoothly in proportion to sensed ram air velocity. At high altitudes, the chute will not open until the seat has descended to 16,404 ft. (5 km.). Always connected to the pilot, the emergency ox-

ygen system built into the seat will provide an adequate air supply either at high altitude or in water in case of a submerged ejection. Optional with the seat is a lateral parting mechanism for peculiar ejection trajectories. This is essential for simultaneous dual ejections. The seat is capable of incorporating a survival kit that includes a crash locator beacon and life support means for differing environmental conditions.

Wings: Simple two-spar structure with titanium load-bearing and carry-through structures. Conventional aluminum alloy skin and miscellaneous subassemblies. The wing is fitted with full-span leading edge flaps and plain half-span inboard flaperons on the slightly swept trailing edge. No ailerons are fitted. The flaperons are capable of deflecting 60° to 70°. Aspect ratio is approximately 3:5. The highly swept wing-root leading edges of the Su-27 are designed to improve wing behavior at high angles of attack, conferring essentially stall-free characteristics, augmenting lift, improving the lift/drag ratio, and retaining stability in roll. The disadvantage to large strakes is that they tend to destabilize an aircraft in the pitch axis, especially at high angles of attack. This can only be tolerated if the instability can be countered with some sort of active flight control system. It is likely that the Su-27's flaps are automatically scheduled by the flight control system during maneuvering to provide a stabilizing function, as well as improving the overall L/D ratio. The Su-27's wing is clearly designed to operate in the transonic region, ruling out any possibility of supersonic cruise performance. The flaps are electrically controlled and have only two positions (up or down) with no intermediate settings.

The fly-by-wire flight control is a four channel analog unit with each control system having its own computer and air data source (externally mounted on the fuselage).

Tail Surfaces: The tail unit consists of twin uncanted vertical stabilizers mounted on narrow decks immediately outboard of the engine housings. Single-piece, hydraulically-actuated, all-moving horizontal stabilators are fitted, and can be deflected differentially or in unison up to 40°.

Leading edge flaps are virtually full-span and appear to be automatically scheduled as part of the aircraft's fly-by-wire flight control system. Blending of fuselage and wing root/chine fairing assembly is readily apparent from this angle. Such blending improves drag characteristics, increases usable internal volume, and has some effect on RCS characteristics.

The Su-27 is a large aircraft for a fighter and is actually somewhat larger than the McDonnell Douglas F-15. Like other fighters, its design is the end product of its radar. Because of the Su-27's long-range intercept mission, the radar's 3 ft. 4 in. (1 m.) diameter flat-plate dish dictated virtually every other feature of the aircraft.

Extreme taper and blending of the Su-27's dynamic fuselage design is readily apparent in this aft view. The vertical tail surfaces have no cant and are perfectly vertical. Extended flaps are noteworthy.

Revealing top view of early production Su-27 provides confirmation that extended tail cone chines of later aircraft with tail warning sensors are a relatively new addition.

All tail surfaces are cantilever all-metal structures. Large ventral fins are mounted below the dorsal verticals, creating a fence-type effect around the aft engine compartment. The ventral fins limit takeoff rotation angle to approx. 17°.

The highly swept vertical stabilizers of the Su-27 are designed to retain their effectiveness at extremely high AoA. This avoids lateral divergence at high AoA, which limits useful lift well below the maximum wing lift on many contemporary fighters. However, comparing the stabilizing effects of the vertical stabilizers, and the destabilizing effects of the fuselage forebody, the relative stabilizing effect of the Su-27's vertical stabilizers is probably somewhat less than that of the F-15. When one considers that the destabilizing influence of the Su-27's fuselage forebody is approximately 30 percent greater than that of the F-15's, it becomes mandatory to have an artificial stability program built into the flight control system. The Su-27 uses active rudders to provide artificial stability on the directional axis. For this reason, the horizontal stabilators, rudders, and flaperons are integrated with each other through the flight control system to provide precise roll and pitch control. Some yaw input is possible through modulation of the powerplants.

Landing Gear: The Su-27 uses a retractable tricycle landing gear, with single wheels fitted to each unit. All three gear retract forward in a conventional manner into their respective gear wells via hydraulic actuators. When the main gear are down, special strut locks connect with faired fittings at the lower outside covers of each engine nacelle. The nose gear is fitted with a mud/FOD guard. The mud guard rotates around the wheel mechanically as the nose gear retracts. The nose gear has an extremely long-stroke levered suspension that allows the aircraft's nose to be lowered quickly after touchdown, so that braking can begin almost immediately. All three landing gear are equipped with hydraulically-actuated disc-type brakes. Hydraulic pressure for these brakes, as noted elsewhere, is variable. The main gear are equipped with integral brake cooling fans inside each gear hub assembly. A drag chute is housed in a covered compartment on the top side of the fuselage tailcone. A large speed-brake is mounted on top of the center fuselage, just aft of the canopy. It is hinged at its forward edge and is activated hydraulically by a single actuator. Speed-brake deployment, which is variable, has a speed limit of .9 Mach. Mainwheel tire size is 40.5 in. (1030 mm.) x 13.7 in. (350 mm.) and tire pressure

"Flanker-D" prototype is equipped with the original "Flanker-B" empennage. The tailhook is mounted underneath and is thought to be hydraulically actuated.

"Flanker-D" is equipped with folding wings, twin-wheel nose landing gear, and retractable inflight refueling probe. Several "Flanker-Ds" have been identified including "59" and "39".

is 12.25-15.7 bars (178 to 227 lb./in.²). Nosewheel tire size is 26.7 in. (680 mm.) x 1.2 in. (260 mm.) and tire pressure 9.3 bars (135 lb./in.²).

Powerplant: The Su-27 is equipped with two Lyulka AL-31F two-shaft augmented turbofan engines rated at 27,560 lbs. th. ea. Mil power is 17,857 lbs. th. ea. The engine is equipped with a single stage afterburner. The inlet is equipped with 23 variable guide vanes. There are four fan stages slotted into their respective discs. The estimated by-pass ratio is .50. The compressor consists of variable inlet guide vanes followed by a nine-stage high-pressure spool with the first three stators being variable. Overall compressor pressure ratio is 24. The engine is equipped with an annular type combustion chamber with 24 downstream burners fed from the inner manifold. The turbine type is a single stage high-pressure unit with air-cooled blades. The low-pressure turbine is a two-stage type. The afterburner has two flameholder rings downstream from the multiple radial spray bars. The afterburner exhaust nozzle assembly consists of interlinked primary and secondary units angled down approximately 5°. The control system is hydromechanical and controlled via software interfacing with the aircraft's fly-by-wire flight control system. All subsystem accessories are driven by power takeoff units and are generally located on the top side of the engine. Left and right side engines are interchangeable. Engine length is 195 in. (4,950 mm.), engine diameter is 48 in. (1,220 mm.), and engine dry weight is 3,373 lb. (1,530 kg.). Specific fuel consumption is .67 lb./hr./lb. th. (18.98 mg./Ns.). Airflow is 247 lbs./sec. Engines have a 1,000 hr. TBO and usually are replaced after 3,000 hrs. AL-31Fs routinely are inspected every 100 hours by borescope, oil analysis, engine vibration monitoring, and other miscellaneous parameters. A test AL-31F has been run on a test stand for over 12,000 hours, indicating the Soviets are working on extending the service life of the basic design. Engine thrust-to-weight ratio is 8:1. This results in a take-off thrust-to-weight ratio of 1.1:1 at the Su-27's normal operating weight of 48,400 lb. (21,954 kg.). The engine exhaust nozzle is fitted with segmented flaps similar to those used by most western convergent-divergent axisymmetric exhaust nozzle designers. The nozzles open extremely wide while the aircraft is on the ground, perhaps as a method of reducing high residual thrust when the throttles are closed. The high thrust rating of the engines enable a take-off run of under 1,700 feet, and the braking parachute

Aeroflax, Inc. collection

It now appears that the navalized version of the Su-27, equipped with canards and referred to as the "Flanker B2", is the Soviet Navy's fighter of choice for forthcoming carrier operations.

Aeroflax, Inc. collection

The only photo released to date of the unidentified side-by-side seating Su-27 variant. This canard-equipped aircraft is thought to be optimized for carrier training.

The P-42 derivative of the "Flanker-B" has set some twenty-seven world time-to-climb records and apparently is being prepared at Ramenskoye for attempts on several others. Stripped of paint, ventral fins, wing and vertical fin tips, and other items, it is considerably lighter than its production stablemates and its engines are thought to be upgraded, as well.

The two-seat Su-27UB is equipped with a vertical-opening, hydraulically-actuated airbrake and a vertically opening canopy, just like the single-seat aircraft. Other than tandem-seating cockpit arrangement, the only readily discernible external difference is the increased height of the vertical fins.

Elevated rear seat and canopy section give the instructor pilot excellent forward visibility in the Su-27UB. Changes between the single-seat and two-seat ''Flanker'' variant are minimal, though the latter does carry slightly less fuel. The Su-27UB remains a viable air combat platform and concedes little to the single-seat aircraft.

allows landing in as little as 1,900 feet. The Su-27, like other Soviet fighter aircraft has a fuel tank nitrogen inerting system to minimize fire danger.

The primary engine air intakes are located under the wing leading edge extensions, where they are shielded to a large extent from the effects of high angles of attack which can cause duct airflow distortion and turbulence. The disadvantage of this location is the long "corner" boundary-layer growth ahead of the intake face. This requires complex diverter paths to get rid of the boundary layer. One surprising feature of the intake design is the closeness of its upper outer corner to the strake edge, which could potentially cause significant interactions between wing flow and intake flow as either lift or engine mass flow is varied. Also, at supersonic speeds the location might be subject to a very complex shock pattern at the intake face, arising from the fuselage, strake and wing shock system converging in this region.

Large auxiliary intake louvers are located in the bottom of each three-ramp duct near the primary wedge-shaped intake. These louvers serve to equalize the pressure differential between the primary ducts and the free air flow, and being spring loaded, can open and close during all stages of flight. Two rows of small vertical louvers for intake mass flow dumping are in each side wall of the wedge, and others are located in its top face. A fine-mesh screen hinges up from the rear-bottom of each duct to shield the engine from foreign object ingestion during take-off and landing at semi-prepared fields. This shield is lowered flush with the bottom surface of the intake after take-off, and is locked into position by a small solenoid located at the intake leading edge.

The T-1 kerosene (or sulfated TS-1) fuel is carried in wing and fuselage tanks, and it is possible for the aircraft to be equipped with a single 400 gal. (1,515 lit.) centerline tank in the narrow groove between the engine nacelles. The inboard wing pylons of late or forthcoming Su-27 variants may be wing tank capable. These are thought to accommodate up to 260 gals. (985 lit.) ea.

Weapons/Sensors: The Su-27 is fitted with a new-generation track-while-scan coherent pulse-Doppler radar with a 3 ft. 4 in. (1 m.) diameter antenna housed in a large, ogival dielectric nose cone. The radar, codenamed *Slot Back* by NATO, does not have the capability to engage multiple targets simultaneously like the latest western fire control radars, but it can track up to ten targets and manually fire weapons at one at a time. The unit has a reported search range of 150 mi. (240 km.) and a tracking range of 115 mi. (185 km.).

A large infrared search and track (IRST) sensor and associated flat collecting mirror (articulated in azimuth and elevation) is located in a faired housing with a fused silica transparency immediately ahead of the windscreen (this unit partially obscures forward visibility). The IRST installation is almost identical to the one used by the MiG-29, although in that aircraft it is offset slightly to the right of centerline. The IRST has a day/night air-to-air search and track capability and is integrated with an air-to-air/air-to-surface laser rangefinder. The laser unit has a spot tracking capability and the IRST is slaveable to the radar and/or helmet mounted sighting system. A general IRST display includes target position data which appears on the cockpit panel CRT and HUD. The IRST provides no target identification capability (no video image display), it has limited air-to-surface capability, and it operates in approximately the 2 to 4 micrometer wavelength band. The helmet mounted target designator also can be used to drive the seeker heads of the AA-10 air-to-air missiles.

The *Sirena*-3 radar warning receivers provide ° coverage from locations outboard of each

The Su-27UB's cockpit sits quite high off the ground but is easily accessed by specially adapted ladders which hang from left side cockpit sill. Canopy is opened and closed hydraulically.

Inflight performance of Su-27UB is claimed to be identical to that of single-seat aircraft. All systems remain essentially the same with the exception of the duplicated instrumentation and controls.

Both variants of the Su-27, including the two-seat Su-27UB are said to have excellent visibility in every direction except directly to the rear. Canopies provide considerable room for pilot movement.

The Su-27UB is a fully capable of accommodating both training and air combat roles. Some limitations on armament complement may exist, however, and it can be presumed that the fuel load has been compromised to accommodate the rear seat. Additionally, the rear seat HUD is non-functional and select items from the front panel had been deleted from the rear.

air intake and at the tail. It operates in the E thru K frequency band range and has a dedicated cockpit display mounted on the instrument panel by the pilot's right knee. It detects and identifies threats, but can provide only directional information and little else.

Various flare and chaff dispensers are located in the extended tailcone of the aircraft. Thirty-two 3-shot cannisters are available.

Two pylons for various air-to-air missiles are installed under each wing, and a similar pylon is installed at each wingtip. The missile on the wingtip pylon is suspended below the pylon, as opposed to outboard of the pylon as in most western designs. A single additional pylon for an air-to-air missile is located on the bottom of each intake trunk. The small area between the engine compartments also can be used to mount air-to-air missiles.

The missile complement available to the Su-27 includes the NATO-designated AA-11 *Archer* (Soviet R-73); the NATO-designated AA-10A/B/C *Alamo* (Soviet R-27); possibly the NATO-designated AA-9 *Amos* (Soviet R-?); and the NATO-designated AA-8 *Aphid* (Soviet R-60). The AA-8 usually is carried on the two outboard wing and wingtip pylons; the AA-9 usually is carried on the two inboard wing pylons; the AA-10 usually is carried on the two inboard wing pylons and all fuselage stations; and the AA-11 usually is carried on the two outboard wing and wingtip pylons. No more than ten missiles can be carried at any one time.

The AA-8 is a close range solid-propellant weapon with infrared homing guidance (some sources indicate that a semi-active radar seeker head has been at least tested on some configurations). It has a canard configuration with small cruciform control surfaces in tandem with nose foreplanes and indexed in-line with the cruciform

rear-mounted wings. The missile is considered to have exceptional maneuverability at close ranges (less than 1,700 ft. [530 m.]).

The AA-10 is the Su-27's primary armament. It is generally similar to the earlier AA-9 in capabilities. It has a complex configuration, with long-span, reverse taper cruciform control surfaces to the rear of and in-line with the small foreplanes. Three different AA-10 versions have been documented to date: *Alamo*-A is a short-burn semi-active radar homing version for use over medium ranges; *Alamo*-B is a medium range infrared version; and *Alamo*-C is a long-burn semi-active radar homing version with greatly increased range.

The AA-11 appears to be a significantly updated version of the AA-2-2 *Atoll* that has long equipped the MiG-21 fighter series, along with almost everything else in the Soviet Air Force. It is a short-range dog-fight missile similar to the American AIM-9 *Sidewinder*.

Though no verifiable information other than a single photograph is available, the Su-27 does have an air-to-ground capability at least in the form of air-to-surface fin-guided rockets. Other weapons, such as the NATO-designated AS-7 *Kerry*, the NATO-designated AS-10 *Karen,* and the NATO-designated AS-12 *Kegler* may be optional. The estimated ordnance capacity of the Su-27 is 17,637 lb. (8,000 kg.) of external stores for the secondary ground attack role.

A single GS-301 30 mm. single-barrel cannon with 149 rounds available is mounted in the starboard wing root extension just aft of the cockpit area. An unpainted titanium blast plate covers the fuselage and surrounding area ahead of and above and below the gun muzzle.

Miscellany: The Su-27 has two separate 4,000 psi hydraulic systems used for the nose wheel steering, landing gear and flap retraction, and brakes. The latter utilize reduced hydraulic pressure of 1,400 psi, though a switch on the control stick allows 2,800 psi for short periods to accommodate engine run-ups prior to takeoff. Large pitot tubes are fitted below the rear edge of the canopy and these provide external sensory data

A single Su-27UB, ''389'' has been assigned the airshow circuit with the single seat aircraft, ''388''. Both often accommodate demonstration requirements. The Su-27UB is seen landing at Oklahoma City.

Jay Miller/Aerofax, Inc.

for the fly-by-wire flight control system and cockpit instrumentation. Various small antenna, undoubtably part of the ECM suite and instrument landing system, are mounted under the forward fuselage, just behind the nose radome. An additional pitot tube is mounted at the front of the radome. An angle-of-attack sensor is located just forward of and above the extreme leading edge of the wing LEX. Small auxiliary air intakes are mounted on the lower leading edge of each vertical stabilizer, while larger pitot tubes are mounted near the top. Large dielectric panels are located at the extreme top of each vertical, and position lights and ECM antennas are located on the trailing edge similar to the F-15. Large dielectric panels, probably for the ECM system, are fitted at the lower outer corner of each intake. The aircraft is IFF-equipped.

ACRONYMS AND ABBREVIATIONS:

AB	Air Base
AEW&C	Airborne Early Warning and Control
AFB	Air Force Base
AoA	angle-of-attack
AWACS	Airborne Warning and Control System
BVR	Beyond Visual Range
CRT	cathode ray tube
DME	distance measuring equipment
DoD	Department of Defense
ECM	electronic countermeasures
EFIS	electronic flight instrumentation system
FBW	fly-by-wire
FLIR	forward looking infrared
FOD	Foreign Object Damage
F.S.	Federal Standard
F.S.D.	full-scale development
ft.	foot/feet
g.	gravity
hr.	hour
HUD	head-up display
IFF	indentification friend or foe
in.	inch/inches
IR	infrared
IRST	infrared search and track
kg.	kilogram
km.	kilometer
km/h	kilometers per hour
lb.	pound/pounds
LR	laser rangefinder
m.	meter
MAI	*Moskovski aviatsionny institut/* Moscow Aviation Institute
MFD	multi-function display
MIG	Mikoyan and Gurevich
mm.	millimeter
mph	miles per hour
NATO	North Atlantic Treaty Organization
OKB	*Opytnoe konstruktorskoe byuro/* Experimental Design Bureau (or Office)
PVO	*Protivovozdushnaya oboronal/* Air Defence
sec.	second
Su	Sukhoi
th.	thrust
TsAGI	*Tsentral'ny aerogidrodinamicheski institut/*Central Aero and Hydrodynamics Institute
TVD	Soviet Theatre of Military Operations
TWS	track-while-scan
UB	*Uchebno-boevoy/*trainer-combat a/c
US	United States
USSR	Union of Soviet Socialist Republics
VVS	*Voenno-vozdushnye sili/* Air Force

The Su-27's massive radar dish is one of the largest currently employed in an operational fighter. Dish size implies considerable burn-through power and thus an increase in "countering" difficulty.

Both the Su-27 single-seater and the Su-27UB were flown to several airshows in the U.S. during 1990, including a major display at Oklahoma City, Oklahoma's Will Rogers Airport.

The leading edge extensions ("lexes") of both the single-seat and two seat "Flankers" (shown) serve to generate vortex flows that help enhance the aircraft's direction stability at high angles of attack.

The **Su-27** prototype, also referred to as the **T-10-1** and/or **"Flanker-A"**, currently is displayed as part of the Soviet Air Force Museum's Sukhoi aircraft collection at Monino northeast of Moscow. At least eight prototypes were built to this drastically different specification and utilized to explore the **"Flanker's"** basic aerodynamics.

Su-27 "Flanker-B", "Blue 388", has been extensively modified for the airshow circuit and has been utilized as the primary demonstration aircraft at Abbottsford, Paris, Farnborough, Oklahoma City, and numerous other locations. Apparently this aircraft has been lightened by removing its radar and other combat related systems.

Su-27 "Flanker-B", "Blue 388", in vertical maneuver during the course of the 1990 Farnborough Airshow. The "Flanker's" extremely high thrust-to-weight ratio gives the aircraft exceptional performance throughout its flight envelope. This capability is enhanced on the special demonstration aircraft as a result of their light weight.

SELECTED DRAWINGS:

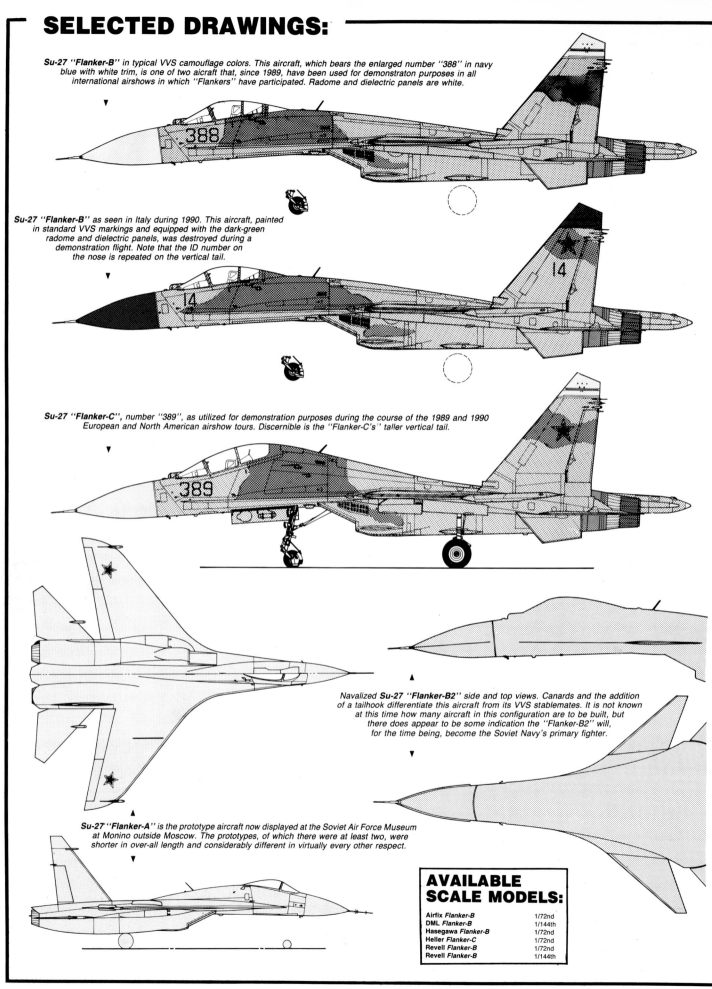

Su-27 "Flanker-B" in typical VVS camouflage colors. This aircraft, which bears the enlarged number "388" in navy blue with white trim, is one of two aircraft that, since 1989, have been used for demonstraton purposes in all international airshows in which "Flankers" have participated. Radome and dielectric panels are white.

Su-27 "Flanker-B" as seen in Italy during 1990. This aircraft, painted in standard VVS markings and equipped with the dark-green radome and dielectric panels, was destroyed during a demonstration flight. Note that the ID number on the nose is repeated on the vertical tail.

Su-27 "Flanker-C", number "389", as utilized for demonstration purposes during the course of the 1989 and 1990 European and North American airshow tours. Discernible is the "Flanker-C's" taller vertical tail.

Navalized *Su-27 "Flanker-B2"* side and top views. Canards and the addition of a tailhook differentiate this aircraft from its VVS stablemates. It is not known at this time how many aircraft in this configuration are to be built, but there does appear to be some indication the "Flanker-B2" will, for the time being, become the Soviet Navy's primary fighter.

Su-27 "Flanker-A" is the prototype aircraft now displayed at the Soviet Air Force Museum at Monino outside Moscow. The prototypes, of which there were at least two, were shorter in over-all length and considerably different in virtually every other respect.

AVAILABLE SCALE MODELS:

Airfix *Flanker-B*	1/72nd
DML *Flanker-B*	1/144th
Hasegawa *Flanker-B*	1/72nd
Heller *Flanker-C*	1/72nd
Revell *Flanker-B*	1/72nd
Revell *Flanker-B*	1/144th

Su-27 FLANKER-B, 'BLUE 388"

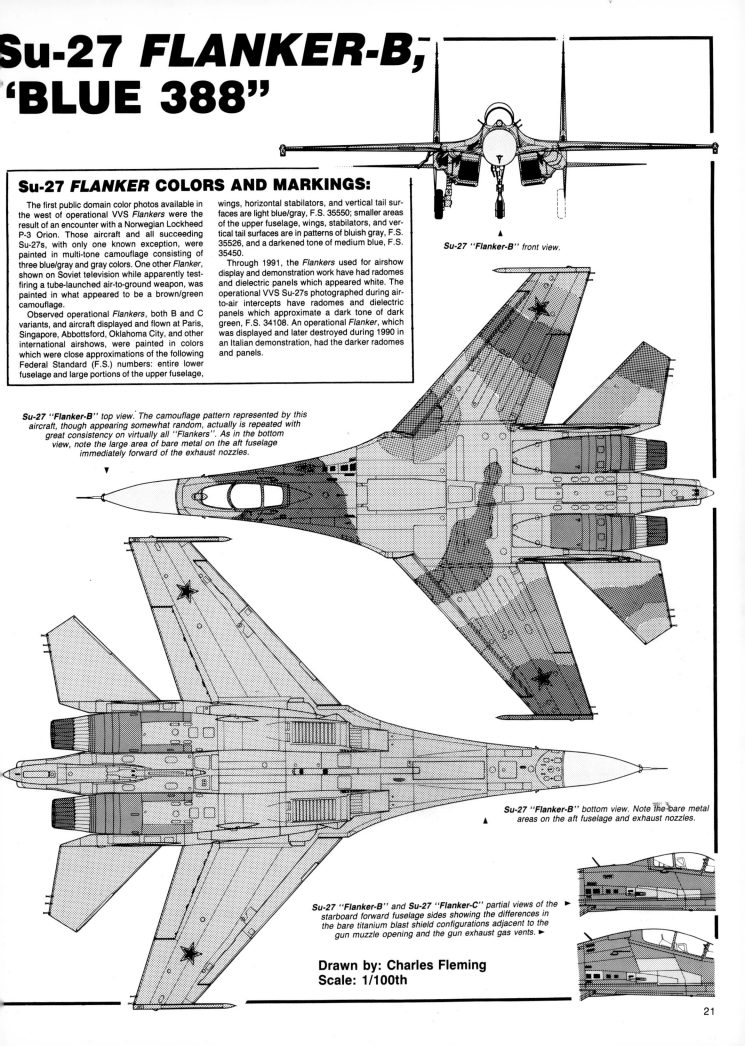

Su-27 FLANKER COLORS AND MARKINGS:

The first public domain color photos available in the west of operational VVS *Flankers* were the result of an encounter with a Norwegian Lockheed P-3 Orion. Those aircraft and all succeeding Su-27s, with only one known exception, were painted in multi-tone camouflage consisting of three blue/gray and gray colors. One other *Flanker*, shown on Soviet television while apparently test-firing a tube-launched air-to-ground weapon, was painted in what appeared to be a brown/green camouflage.

Observed operational *Flankers*, both B and C variants, and aircraft displayed and flown at Paris, Singapore, Abbottsford, Oklahoma City, and other international airshows, were painted in colors which were close approximations of the following Federal Standard (F.S.) numbers: entire lower fuselage and large portions of the upper fuselage,

wings, horizontal stabilators, and vertical tail surfaces are light blue/gray, F.S. 35550; smaller areas of the upper fuselage, wings, stabilators, and vertical tail surfaces are in patterns of bluish gray, F.S. 35526, and a darkened tone of medium blue, F.S. 35450.

Through 1991, the *Flankers* used for airshow display and demonstration work have had radomes and dielectric panels which appeared white. The operational VVS Su-27s photographed during air-to-air intercepts have radomes and dielectric panels which approximate a dark tone of dark green, F.S. 34108. An operational *Flanker*, which was displayed and later destroyed during 1990 in an Italian demonstration, had the darker radomes and panels.

Su-27 "Flanker-B" front view.

Su-27 "Flanker-B" top view. The camouflage pattern represented by this aircraft, though appearing somewhat random, actually is repeated with great consistency on virtually all "Flankers". As in the bottom view, note the large area of bare metal on the aft fuselage immediately forward of the exhaust nozzles.

Su-27 "Flanker-B" bottom view. Note the bare metal areas on the aft fuselage and exhaust nozzles.

Su-27 "Flanker-B" and Su-27 "Flanker-C" partial views of the starboard forward fuselage sides showing the differences in the bare titanium blast shield configurations adjacent to the gun muzzle opening and the gun exhaust gas vents. ►

Drawn by: Charles Fleming
Scale: 1/100th

*Differences in the "**Flanker-B**" and "**Flanker-C**" center around the cockpit area. The "**Flanker-C**" is equipped with a slightly elevated instructor's seat and associated controls and instrumentation. Other changes are somewhat more subtle and include taller vertical tail surfaces and a reduced fuel capacity.*

*The "**Flanker-C**", also referred to as the **Su-27UB,** has an extended canopy to accommodate the second, rear crew seat. It remains fully combat capable and can carry essentially the same armament complement found on the standard single-seat "**Flanker-B**". Noteworthy in this view is the extended tow bar with independent castor assembly.*

"Flanker-B", "Red 14", demonstrated in Italy during 1990. The dark green radome and dark green dielectric panels appear to be standard for operational aircraft, as does camouflage.

"Flanker-B" cockpit is equipped with primarily analog instrumentation. HUD is centrally mounted above main panel combing. Radar CRT and radar warning panel are visible to right.

"Flanker-B", "Red 14" during its Italian demonstration tour. This aircraft was lost during the course of an aerobatic performance on Sept. 9, 1990, and the pilot, Rimas Stankiavicius of Gromov Flight Research Institute, was fatally injured. It is believed that this was the first time ever that an operational Su-27 had been placed on pulbic display in the west.

Operational ''Flanker-B'', ''41'', on what appears to be a dirt strip somewhere in the Soviet Union. The Su-27, like most Soviet aircraft, is cleared for rough field operations. This ''Flanker-B'' is somewhat unusually equipped with a white radome and dark green vertical fin tips while bearing the standard grey on blue-grey camouflage.

Planform view of ''Flanker-B'' provides insight into deceivingly simple wing geometry. Leading and trailing edge devices, which apparently are integrated into the aircraft's fly-by-wire flight control system, coupled with complex wing twist and blending, result in an exceptionally strong and aerodynamically sophisticated aerodynamic surface.

Lightly loaded, the Su-27's takeoff and landing performance is phenomenal. This is due to the aircraft's exceptionally high thrust-to-weight ratio and its efficient aerodynamics. Air-show circuit aircraft, such as "Flanker-B" "388" and "Flanker-C" "389" almost certainly have been stripped of their radar systems to improve performance even more.

photo almost certainly represents the first image published in the west of the T-10-24 testbed aircraft. This "Flanker" variant has been optimized for long-range missions and, like the navalized "Flanker-D" is equipped with a retractable refueling probe. Noteworthy in this view are extended probe and offset IRST-system sensor fairing.

Extreme aft placement of the nose landing gear requires an exceptionally long tow-bar for ground maintenance operations. Tow-bar is equipped with safety cables which apparently spread the drag loads to the main gear, as well as the nose unit. Similar to western practices, cockpit is manned at all times during towing process.

Most of the major air-to-air missiles in the Soviet Air Force inventory can be carried by the Su-27. Both long and short burn AA-10 "Alamos" are shown in this view, with the wing pylon-mounted and aft centerline missiles being equipped with infrared homing seeker heads, and the other missiles apparently being radar seeker head equipped.

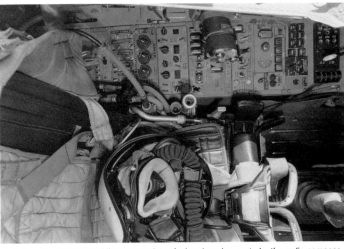

Left console of "Flanker-B" accommodates fuel and engine controls, the radio compass panel, the oxygen mix panel, flap controls, and miscellaneous indicators.

Jay Miller/Aerofax, Inc.

Jay Miller/Aerofax, Inc.

Standard "Flanker-B" main instrument panel includes centrally mounted head-up display and radar CRT (to right). Instrumentation is almost totally analog.

Right console of "Flanker-B" accommodates environmental system controls, warning panel push switches, and some weapon systems controls. To far left is radar warning panel.

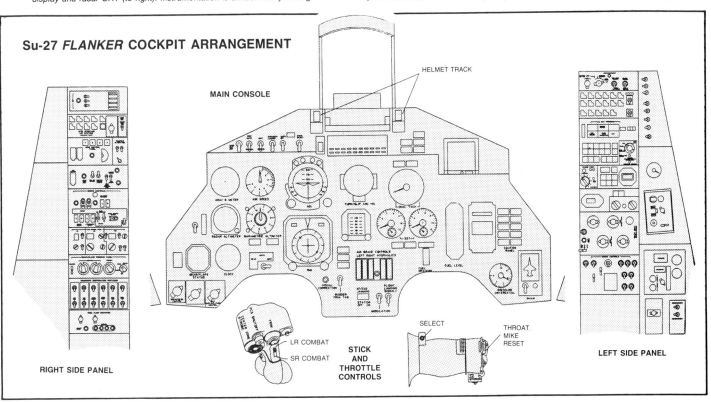

Su-27 *FLANKER* COCKPIT ARRANGEMENT

HELMET TRACK

MAIN CONSOLE

RIGHT SIDE PANEL

STICK AND THROTTLE CONTROLS

LEFT SIDE PANEL

LR COMBAT
SR COMBAT

SELECT
THROAT MIKE RESET

"Flanker-C" front seat left console echoes panel layouts and throttle quadrant design of single-seat aircraft. Oxygen and communications systems connections are visible.

"Flanker-C" front seat right console echoes panel layouts found on single-seat aircraft. Warning panel push-switch panel is readily discernible.

Main instrument panel of "Flanker-C" is equipped with conventional HUD assembly. Instrumentation and radar CRT to right (behind mask) are identical to "Flanker-B".

Su-27 *FLANKER* OBSCURATION OF PILOT VISION

DESIGN EYE:
ES 205.13
WL 156.57

11.00 DEG.

ELEVATION (DEGREES)

AZIMUTH (DEGREES)

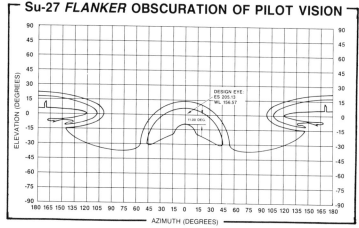

"Flanker-C" back seat left console is considerably more spartan than that of front seat. Linear throttle quadrant is mounted on cockpit wall, rather than console.

"Flanker-C" back seat main instrument panel is virtually identical to front seat with exception of non-functional HUD. Noteworthy is radar CRT to right.

"Flanker-C" back seat right console emulates that of front seat and includes what appears to be a duplicate radar warning panel (center, top).

Aerofax, Inc. collection

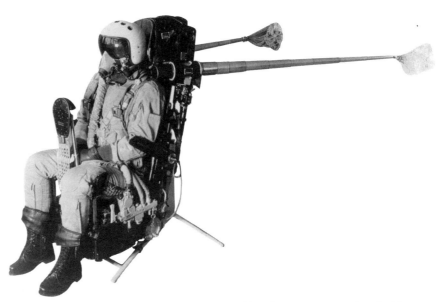

Rocket-propelled K-36DM ejection seat is utilized in several Soviet combat aircraft including the MIG-29.

Zero-zero K-36DM rocket-propelled ejection seat provides safe emergency egress throughout the Su-27's flight envelope. It is equipped with stabilizing drogue chutes.

Jay Miller/Aerofax, Inc.

Aerofax, Inc. collection

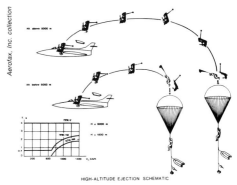

HIGH-ALTITUDE EJECTION SCHEMATIC

Zero-zero K-36DM ejection seat provides safe emergency egress throughout the Su-27s flight envelope.

Jay Miller/Aerofax, Inc.

"Flanker-B" front K-36DM ejection seat headrest and drogue-arm cylinder assemblies.

"Flanker-C" front K-36DM ejection seat headrest and drogue-arm cylinder assemblies.

T-10 main instrument panel was highly simplified in light of prototype requirements.

Aerofax, Inc. collection

Testing of the K-36DM ejection seat apparently was undertaken utilizing a modified Sukhoi Su-11 with a special second, aft cockpit.

"Flanker-B" canopy and windscreen consist of three transparencies. Canopy transparencies are split by single hoop structure. Windscreen is one-piece unit.

"Flanker-C" canopy and windscreen differ in contour from those of "Flanker-B", but remain similar in having a total of three transparencies. Note rearview mirrors.

"Flanker-C" rear seat headrest is recessed aft under metal part of canopy structure.

"Flanker-C" canopy is hydraulically actuated and hinged aft. Access to cockpit is via conventional ladders with attachment hooks above top rung.

Single-piece windscreen and aft-hinged canopy of T-10-1 prototype. Noteworthy is absence of faired IRST sensor ahead of windscreen.

Ingress/egress ladders are dedicated to the Su-27. Their coloring generally appears to be orange. Note bumper under forward edge of LEX.

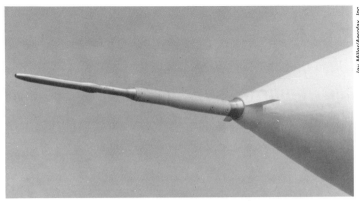

At pitot fairing point at nose cone tip, a small ring with vortex-generating vanes is attached. These reportedly make a considerable contribution to pitch stability.

Angle-of-attack sensor vane, reminiscent of western designs is mounted on each side of Su-27's nose, beneath windscreen. Dielectric panel is visible to left.

Titanian gun blast deflector shield replaces conventional aluminum skin around and just ahead of gun barrel. Large static pitot is visible upper center.

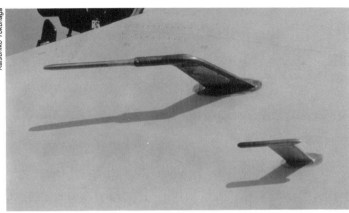

Fly-by-wire flight control system requires input from a large number of static pitot sources. There are at least five visible and there may be others.

There have been several variations to the Su-27's empennage design. Current version includes strakes that terminate in dielectric covers for tail warning sensors.

The 30 mm. single-barrel cannon is mounted on the right side of the aircraft. The titanium blast shield ahead of the muzzle is always left unpainted.

Empennage also accommodates drag chute compartment, chaff and flare ejection cannisters (on top), and apparently fuel tanks.

Jay Miller/Aerofax, Inc.

Ventral view of fuselage from empennage looking forward. Wide space between engine nacelles serves as mounting point for up to two air-to-air missiles.

Ventral view of fuselage from edge of intakes looking aft. Mounting lugs and associated fairings for central missile pylons are readily visible.

Some Su-27s are equipped with a small, retractable release handle probably associated with the drag chute and or drag chute compartment.

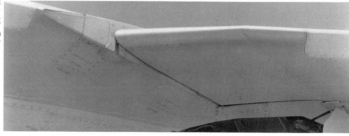

Katsuhiko Tokunaga

The interface point between the wing leading edge root (leading edge flap) and the LEX are not faired. Noteworthy is the small notch for flap limit pin.

The Su-27 is equipped with a full-span leading edge flap. Its actuation is integrated into the aircraft's fly-by-wire flight control system.

The single-piece trailing edge flaps also provide limited roll control imput and thus can technically be referred to as flaperons.

The leading edge flap is connected to the wing via multiple hinges along the lower lip of flap trailing edge. It is hydraulically actuated.

The trailing edge flaps are hydraulically actuated and are integrated with the aircraft's fly-by-wire flight control system.

The Su-27UB's vertical tail surfaces are taller than those of the single-seat aircraft.

"Flanker-B's" rudders are assumed to be hydraulically actuated. Rudders have four hinges.

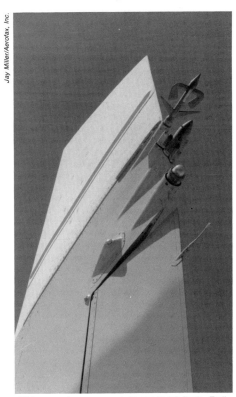

Dielec. panel covers com. antennas in left fin tip. Trailing edge mounts radar warning and nav. antennas.

Jay Miller/Aerofax, Inc.

Katsuhiko Tokunaga

Jay Miller/Aerofax, Inc.

Jay Miller/Aerofax, Inc.

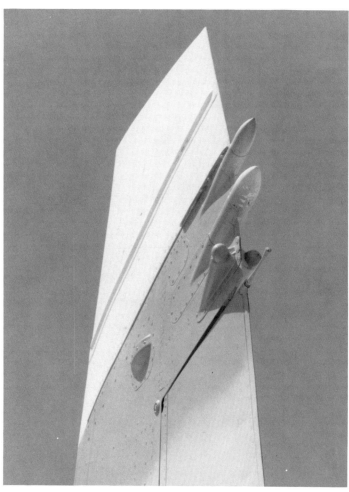

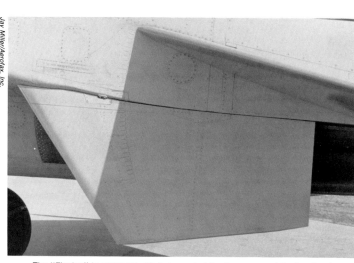

The "Flanker" is equipped with large ventral fins to accommodate directional stability requirements at high angles-of-attack and low airspeed.

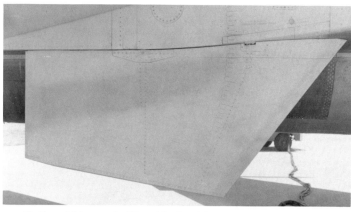

Dielec. panel covers com. antennas in right fin tip. Other antennas include radar warning and navigation systems (top).

Markings visible on vertical fin and fuselage fairing structure indicate horizontal stabilator incidence maximum throw angles (14° up and 21° down).

"Flanker's" slab stabilator is a single-piece unit that serves to impart both pitch and roll inputs. Symmetrical action imparts pitch moment and asymmetrical input imparts roll moment.

T-10-1 actuator fairings are offset from bases of vertical tails and conceal small hydraulic rams.

Static discharge units are fixed and rigid and easily removed or replaced.

Stabilators have surface area inside of the vertical tail attachment fairing.

Jay Miller/Aerofax, Inc.

Jay Miller/Aerofax, Inc.

Su-27UB nose landing gear is structurally identical to that of single-seat aircraft.

Su-27UB nose landing gear is optimized for rough field operations.

Su-27UB nose landing gear mud guard is designed to prevent engine FOD.

Katsuhiko Tokunaga

Tom Copeland collection

Finned lower aft section of mud guard for Su-27UB lowers drag and permits foreign object drainage.

Heavy duty "Flanker-B" nose gear differs only in design of mud guard.

"Flanker-B" (and "C") mud guard is articulated to compensate for fork movement.

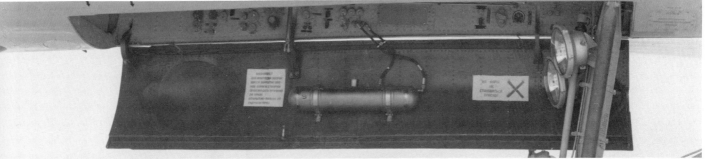

Nose landing gear well cover for "Flanker" has dual hinges and pneumatic closing system integrated with nose gear retraction sequence. Pneumatic reservoir is attached to door. Nose gear has extremely long stroke levered suspension system to permit rapid deceleration following touchdown and efficient utilization of aerodynamic as well as mechanical braking.

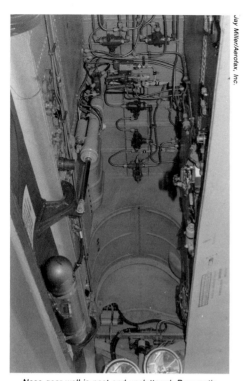

Nose gear well is neat and uncluttered. Pneumatic door actuator is visible center left.

Main landing gear retract forward into their respective wells. Note down-lock and fairing.

Main landing gear is equipped with an integral cooling fan to accommodate heavy braking requirements.

Main gear well is covered by two pneumatically opened and closed doors. Each door is attached by two hinge assemblies.

Main gear and associated strut assemblies are designed for rough field operations. Retraction sequence is hydraulically actuated.

Main gear wheel and tire assembly fit into enlarge forward segment of well. Typical of this aircraft, the wells are uncluttered and neat.

Forward bay of main gear well has independent door with separate pneumatic actuator. Noteworthy in this view is electrical connector for EW sensor.

Katsuhiko Tokunaga

Left main gear well. Visible lower rt. is down lock assembly and associated fuselage attachment point. Noteworthy is large hydraulic ram (upper lt.).

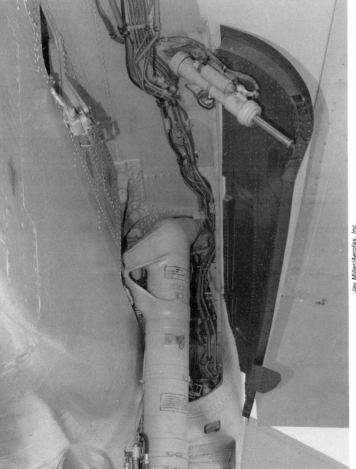

Main gear has only one swivel or hinge point. Gear retraction is sequenced with gear well doors and their associated pneumatic rams.

Jay Miller/Aerofax, Inc.

Intakes are ventrally located for maximum efficiency throughout the aircraft's flight envelope. Nacelle slab sides taper into rounded aft fairings.

Extremely angled intake lip configuration provides excellent ram recovery at various angles-of-attack while also permitting ramps to control shock formation.

Intakes are equipped with a variety of bleed slots and variable ramp doors—all for mass flow and shock wave control. Boundary layer slot is visible at top.

The intakes are equipped with automatic, pneumatically retractable FOD protection screens which are hinged at the bottom of each intake throat.

Compressor section face of Lyulka AL-31F turbofan engine is readily visible at end of intake tunnel with FOD screen in retracted position.

A number of spring-loaded auxiliary intake slats makes up the ventral side of the intake box. These open and close automatically upon propulsion system demand.

Inertial navigation system and related mission programing panels are located behind a fuselage access panel just ahead underneath the left side forward LEX.

Two Lyulka AL-31F afterburning turbofan engines power the "Flanker". Engine dry weight is approximately 3,373 lb. (1,530 kg.) and max. thrust in afterburner is 27,560 lb. (12,501 kg.). The AL-31F has a relatively high (for a Soviet engine) TBO in excess of a thousand hours. The AL-31F gives the Su-27 a very high thrust-to-weight ratio.

Exhaust interior and afterburner ignition rings of AL-31F. Engine estimated by-pass ratio is 50—which is relatively high, even by western standards.

Jay Miller/Aerofax, Inc.

Engine exhaust nozzles are neatly faired at the end of each engine nacelle. Exhaust nozzle flap assembly is clean with a dual set of interfacing feathers.

Engine nacelles are complex geometrical structures suspended from fuselage carry-through assemblies. Fuselage empennage taper is extreme.

Katsuhiko Tokunaga

Single-barrel GS-301 30 mm. cannon is mounted on aircraft right side and is somewhat crudely faired with its muzzle protruding over a titanium blast plate.

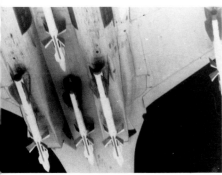

Two short burn (centerline) and two long burn AA-10 "Alamo" air-to-air missiles.

Su-27 *FLANKER* AA-10 *ALAMO* FAMILY

AA-10A SEMI ACTIVE SHORT BURN
(CARRIED ON MIG-29 AND Su-27)

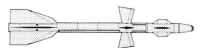

AA-10B INFRARED SHORT BURN
(CARRIED ON MIG-29 and Su-27)

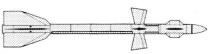

AA-10C RADAR SEMI ACTIVE LONG BURN
(CARRIED ON Su-27 ONLY)

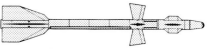

AA-10C INFRARED SEMI ACTIVE LONG BURN
(CARRIED ON Su-27 ONLY)

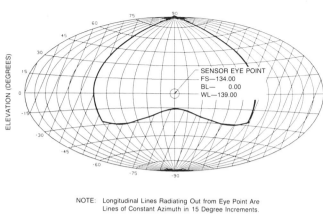

OBSCURATION PLOT FOR Su-27 NOSE SENSOR

SENSOR EYE POINT
FS—134.00
BL—   0.00
WL—139.00

ELEVATION (DEGREES)

NOTE: Longitudinal Lines Radiating Out from Eye Point Are
Lines of Constant Azimuth in 15 Degree Increments.

T-10-1 prototypes were equipped with aerodynamically refined mass balances inset from tapered wingtips. They also had inboard wing fences.

Wing tip missile rail normally is utilized to carry the AA-11 "Archer" infrared-guided air-to-air missile; some sources claim AA-10s also can be carried.

Operational "Flanker" variants are presumed equipped with IRST sensor ball mounted just ahead of windscreen. Laser designator may be integrated into this unit.

Apparently part of the "Sirena" radar warning antenna complement, a dielectic fairing protrudes from the side of each forward intake box assembly. Configuration indicates 90° coverage for this particular antenna.

THE Su-27 FLANKER CONTROL-STICK

Interchanging Gun/Missile Triggers on the Front of the Stick-Grip

"Bring Level" Auto-Pilot Engage, Data-Link Couple

"SDU Off" Auto-Pilot/ Data-Link Couple Disengage

Pitch/Roll Trim

"Long Range" Battle "Short Range"

"Center of the Strobe Zon" Cursor Slew Control

Su-27 control stick serves as mounting point for several weapon and flight control system inputs.

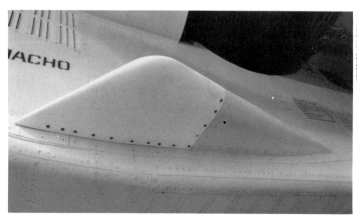

Intake-mounted "Sirena" radar warning antenna fairing is mostly dielectric material with a metal aft fairing segment added apparently for strength reasons.

Chaff and flare dispenser units are mounted in the empennage area side chines. Others are mounted on the empennage centerline ahead of the EW antennas.